Hooray for Eiley!
You make the world a happy
and loving place.
~ Love and Squishy Squeezy Bear Hugs to You ~
Kathy Greenberg

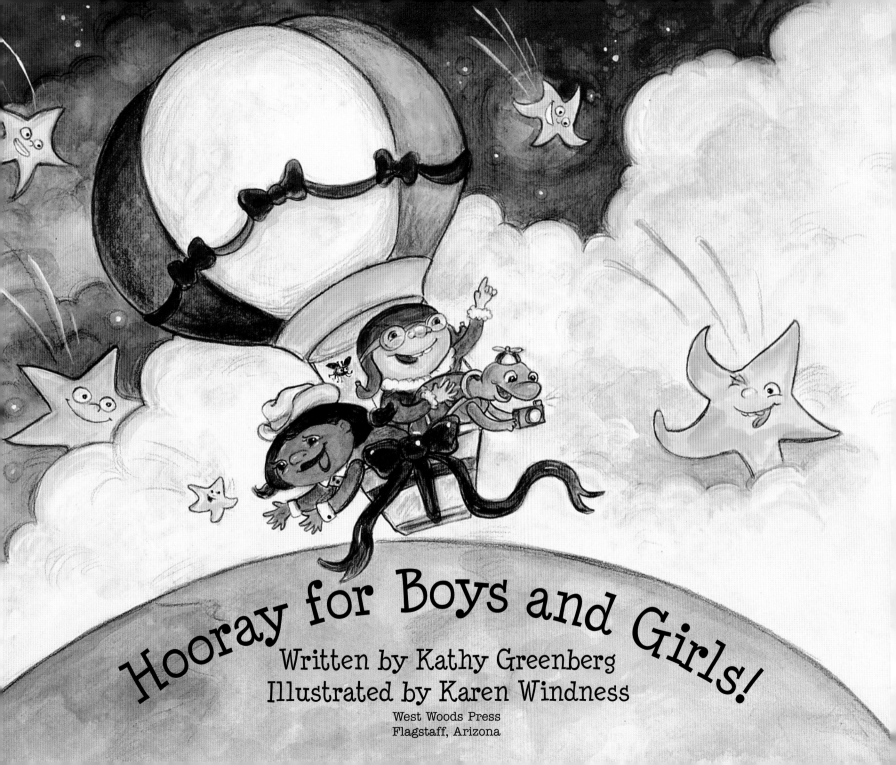

Hooray for Boys and Girls!

Written by Kathy Greenberg
Illustrated by Karen Windness

West Woods Press
Flagstaff, Arizona

The artwork was created in pastel, oil, watercolor, acrylic and colored pencil, on 200 lb. hot press Arches watercolor paper. The text was set in Minya Nouvelle™ by Ray Larabie. Book layout and design by Karen Windness. Digital photography and pre-press by Colorline, Lakewood, CO.

Publisher's Cataloging-in-Publication Data (Provided by Quality Books, Inc.)

Greenberg, Kathy, 1961-
Hooray for boys and girls! / written by Kathy Greenberg ; illustrated by Karen Windness – 1st ed. p. cm.
SUMMARY: Two children, a turtle and a ladybug travel around the world in a hot air balloon, visiting people of many cultures, land and sea animals, the sun and moon. Everyone and everything welcomes them with celebration. Animals play silly games and people sing, dance and play musical instruments.
Audience: Ages 3-7.
LCCN 2005938226
ISBN 0-9776837-0-2

1. Children–Social aspects–Juvenile fiction. 2. Respect for persons–Juvenile fiction. 3. Flights around the world–Juvenile fiction. [1. Children–Fiction. 2. Turtle–Fiction. 3. Ladybug–Fiction. 4. Hot air balloons–Fiction. 5. Travel–Fiction. 6. Cheerfulness–Fiction. 7. Toleration—Fiction.]
I. Windness, Karen. II. Title.

PZ8.3.G757Hor 2006   [E] QBI05-600212

Published in the United States of America
Printed in Korea

To my children,
Jeremy, Alissa and Alex,
with love.
K.G.

For my nephew, Kail.
K.W.

To all our Earth's children who make
the world a beautiful place.
K.G. and K.W.

When boys and girls are near,
the most amazing things begin to happen...

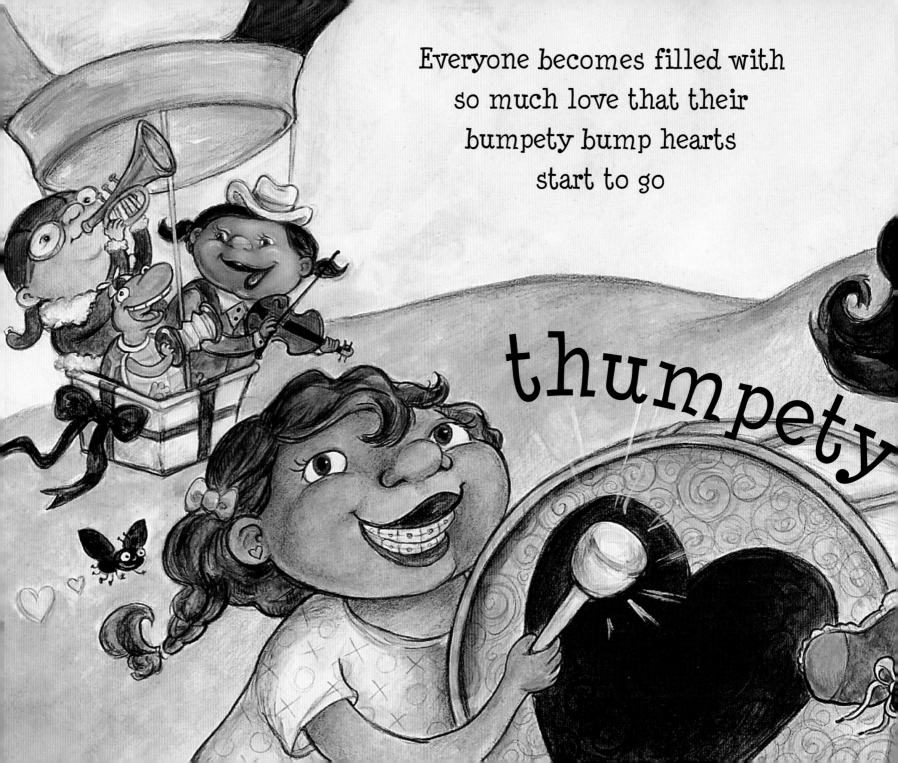

Everyone becomes filled with
so much love that their
bumpety bump hearts
start to go

thumpety

humpety thump thump thump.

Sad people who slippity slump

turn into smiling people who jippity jump.

Cranky people who
snippity snap

turn into giggling people
who clippity clap.

Folks whistle catchy tunes like "Rummy-Tum-Tum" and hum happy songs like "Fiddle Dee Dum."

Fingers start to snap,
and tummies start to jiggle.

Toes begin to tap,
then hips start to wiggle.

Parents bounce
babies like bunnies
on their lippity laps

and dance to
happy songs like
the
"Bounce-A-Baby
Rap."

When children arrive...

The man in the moon
opens his sleepy eyes
and sings

"Tra La Lune."

The sun wraps children in
warm, cozy hugs and croons,
"Come back soon."

When girls and boys are close by...

Dolphins flippity flop with whales in the salty seas.

Kangaroos hippity hop with
the buzzing bumble bees.

Kitties whisper
"Yummy in my tummy"
as they sip their catnip tea.

Monkeys shout "Bumpy Monkey Mamm

The world becomes a happy and exciting place when children are near.

The reason is quite clear.

It's because boys and girls are gifts to the world!

Children come in lots of fun shapes, colors, and sizes.

They decorate our world;
they're full of surprises.

Boys and girls can build wacky hairdos and make funny faces.

They love to
wiggle-waggle walk
in baby diaper races.

Children paint pretty pictures, and
people smile from ear to ear.
They give "squishy squeezy"
bear hugs that last for
years and years.

The kindness in
children's hearts
makes our world
    a loving place.
        Their giggles and wiggles give our world a happy face.

"Hip, Hip, Hooray!"
for children of the world!

They're gifts that play
with us and dream
for us and love
us into joy.

Our world is complete
because of every girl and boy.

"Bounce-A-Baby-Rap"

Bumpety bump and thumpety thump,
Slippity slump and jippity jump,
Rummy-tum-tum and fiddle dee dum,
Hippity hop and flippity flop,
Jiggle and snap and wiggle and tap,
Let's all dance to the
"Bounce-A-Baby Rap."